W9-CQD-988

MAZES

Also available from Grosset & Dunlap, Publishers

ABC MAZES
ASTRO MAZES
DINOSAUR MAZES
HAUNTED MAZES
MYSTERY MAZES
SHARKMAZE
TRAVEL MAZES
MAZES FOR FUN 1
MAZES FOR FUN 2
MAZES FOR FUN 3
MAZES FOR FUN 4

FOR ADULTS:
MAZES
MAZES 2
MAZES 3
MAZES 4
MAZES 5
MAZES 6

MAZES
BY VLADIMIR KOZIAKIN

GROSSET & DUNLAP
PUBLISHERS/NEW YORK

Dedicated to
my father
Barrie
and the Frog
for their patience

Copyright © 1971 by Vladimir Koziakin.
All rights reserved.
Published simultaneously in Canada.
ISBN: 0-448-01836-5

Manufactured in the United States of America.

INTRODUCTION

Mazes are ancient devices. Legend has it that the first was built by the Athenian craftsman Daedalus to house the sacred bull of the King of Crete. Each year the cream of Athenian youth was fed into the labyrinth to be devoured by the bull until the hero Theseus went in and killed the monster.

Since that time mazes have been associated with far more peaceful pursuits. Elaborate mazes of high, well-tended hedges decorated the estates of Europe, England, and Colonial America, in which guests amused themselves by trying to find their way out. Those mazes were usually of a gracious but conventional geometric design.

The mazes presented here are far more free, more amorphous and contemporary, but they still pose the same exit problem. The point is, of course, still to find your way out, and if a contestant feels hopelessly lost (or wishes to verify that there is indeed a way out), he can refer to the solutions in the back of the book.

To heighten competition, each maze has been assigned a rated time limit. However, it would be well to keep in mind that time is highly subjective. You may whip through one maze in nothing flat and then find yourself bogged down for days in another yet no more difficult one.

In solving these mazes you may wish to place a piece of tracing paper over them and draw your route on the tracing paper. In addition to being convenient, tracing paper crumples with a fierce noise, soothing frustration as effectively as screaming and far less dangerously than kicking the furniture or woodwork. If solving them gets to be too much of a hassle, rip them out and paste them on the wall. In any event, good luck!

Vladimir Koziakin

Maze 1

SALAMANDER

| Rated Time Limit: | 2 Minutes |

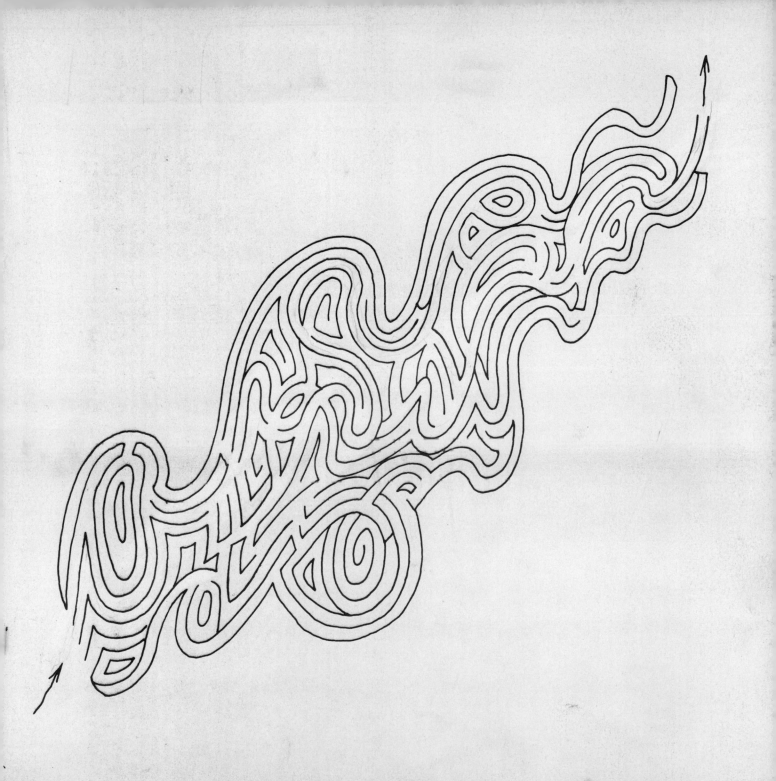

Maze 2
CEREBELLUM
Rated Time Limit: | 5 Minutes

Maze 3

QUASIMODO

Rated Time Limit: | **5½ Minutes**

Maze 4

AMOEBA

Rated Time Limit: | **6 Minutes**

Maze 5

CIRCLET

Rated Time Limit: | **8 Minutes**

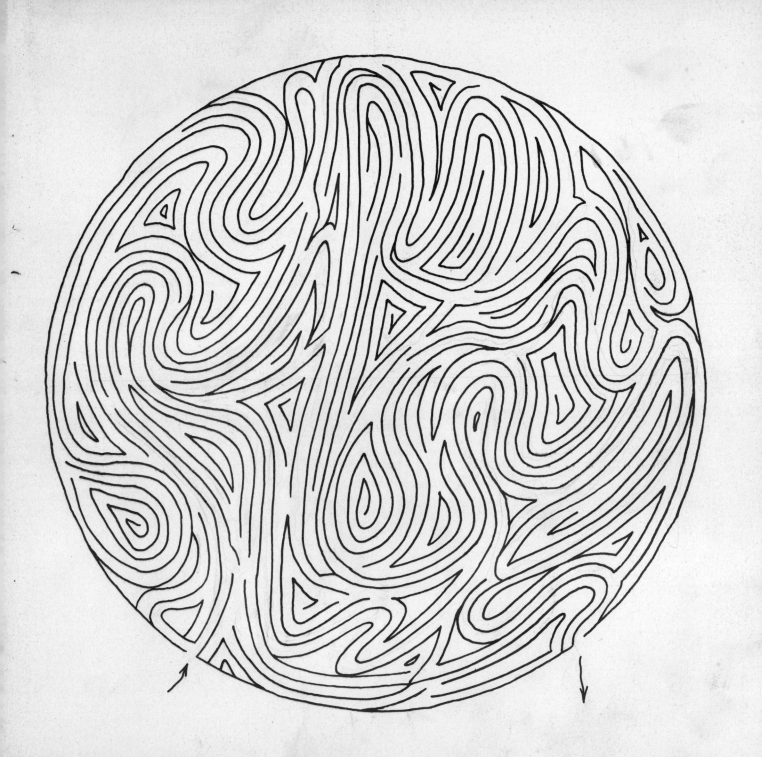

Maze 6

COIFFURE

Rated Time Limit: | *10 Minutes*

Maze 7

BLOCKHOUSE

Rated Time Limit: | **10 Minutes**

Maze 8

QUETZALCOATL

| *Rated Time Limit:* | *10 Minutes* |

Maze 9
UNDULATION
Rated Time Limit: | **10 Minutes**

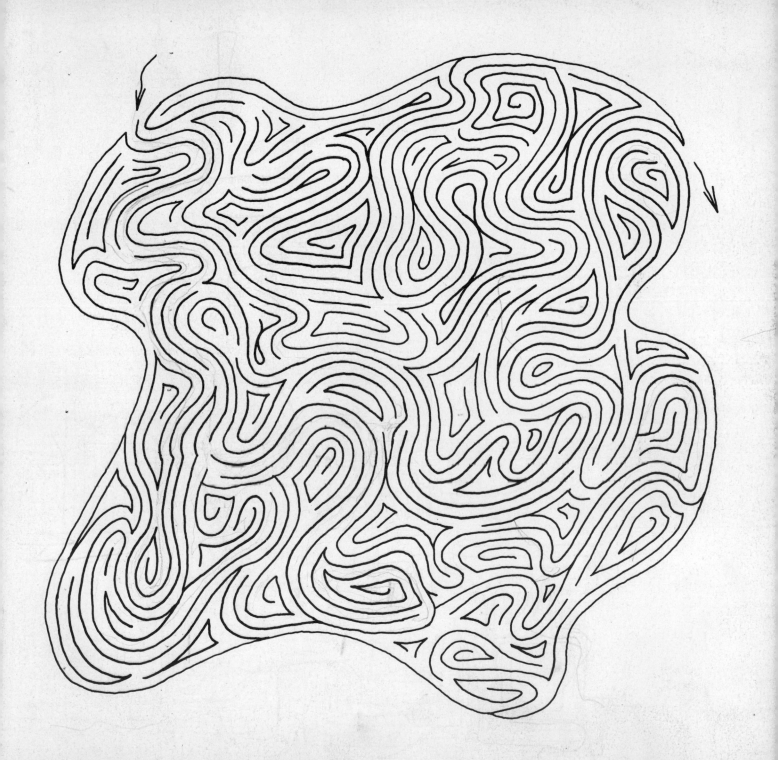

Maze 10

THE MINES OF MORIA

Rated Time Limit: | **10 Minutes**

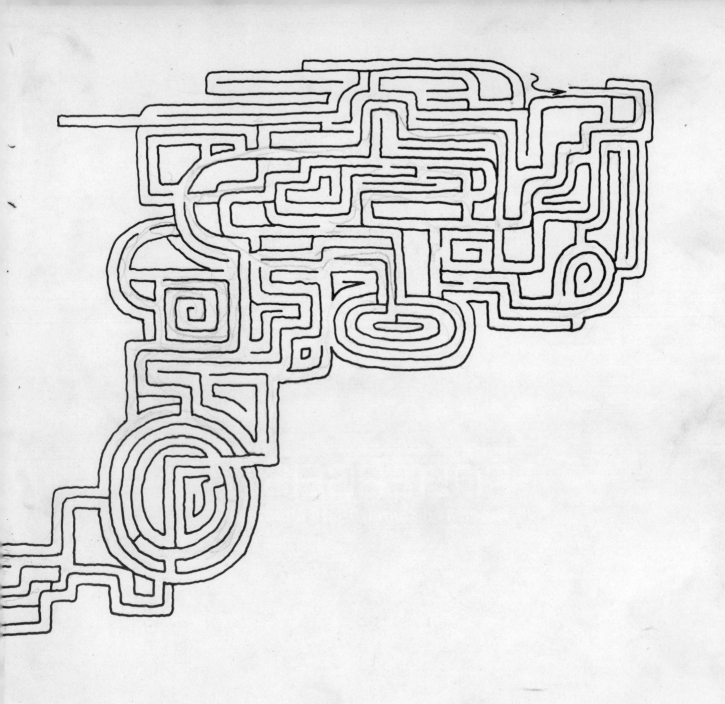

Maze 11

POLTERGEIST

Rated Time Limit: | **10 Minutes**

Maze 12

ARROWHEAD

Rated Time Limit: | 10 Minutes

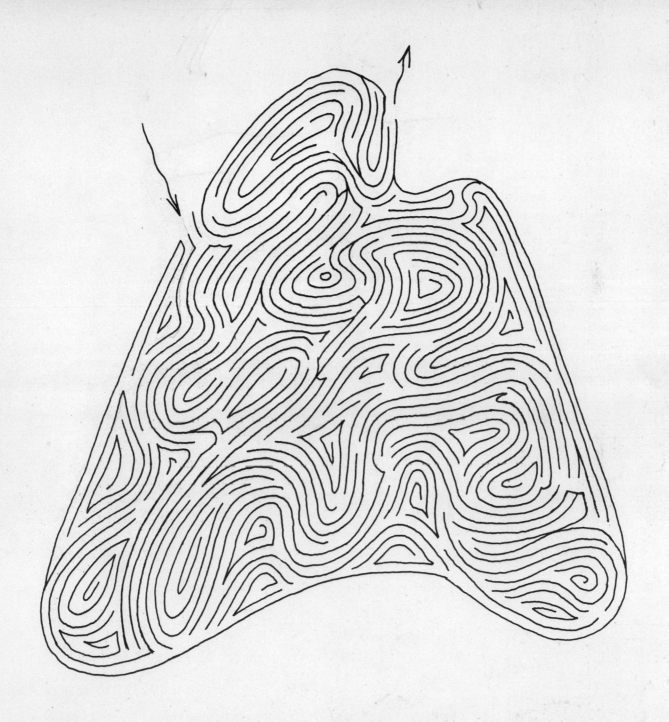

Maze 13

TADPOLE

Rated Time Limit: | *10 Minutes*

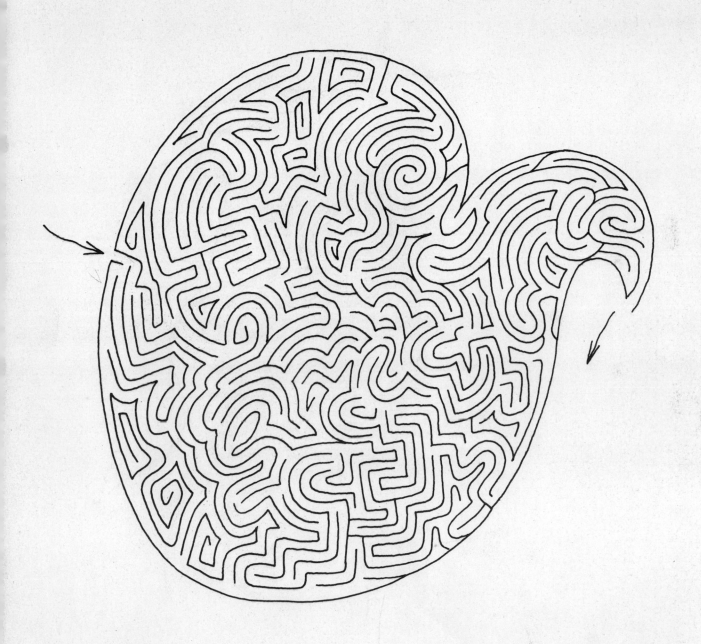

Maze 14
FREEDOM
Rated Time Limit: | 15 Minutes

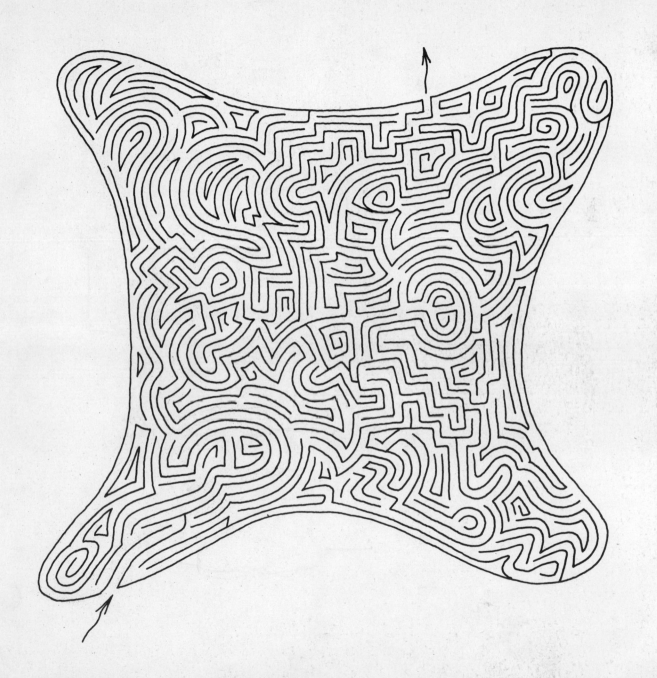

LABYRINTH

Rated Time Limit: | **15 Minutes**

BLOB

Rated Time Limit: | **15 Minutes**

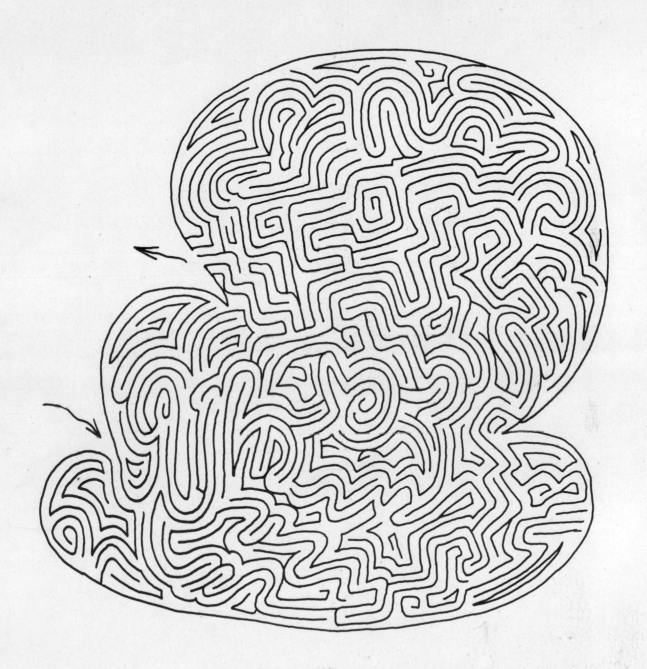

GASP

Rated Time Limit: | **16 Minutes**

Maze 18

CUMULUS

Rated Time Limit: | **18 Minutes**

APPARITION

Rated Time Limit: | **18 Minutes**

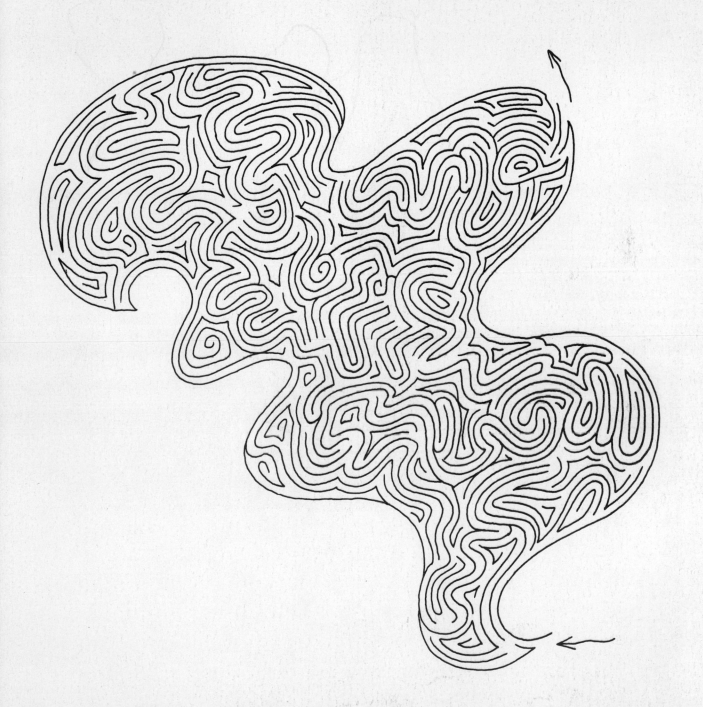

Maze 20

MAELSTROM

Rated Time Limit: | **18 Minutes**

Maze 21

AERIAL VIEW

Rated Time Limit: | **19 Minutes**

Maze 22

TRIPLE-DECKER UPSIDE-DOWN SPEECH BALLOON

Rated Time Limit: *19 Minutes*

Maze 23

BEWILDERED

Rated Time Limit: | **28 Minutes**

Maze 24

MINOTAUR'S LAIR

Rated Time Limit: | **28 Minutes**

Maze 25

GARGOYLE

| Rated Time Limit: | 30 Minutes |

Maze 26
SENTRY

| Rated Time Limit: | 35 Minutes |

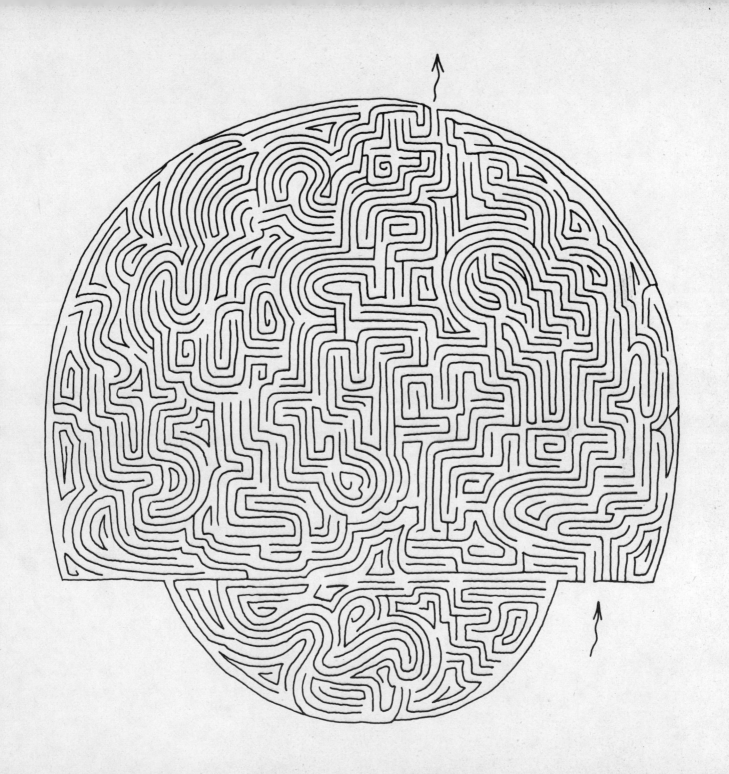

Maze 27

RORSCHACH

Rated Time Limit: | **35 Minutes**

Maze 28
RHINOCEROS
Rated Time Limit: | **40 Minutes**

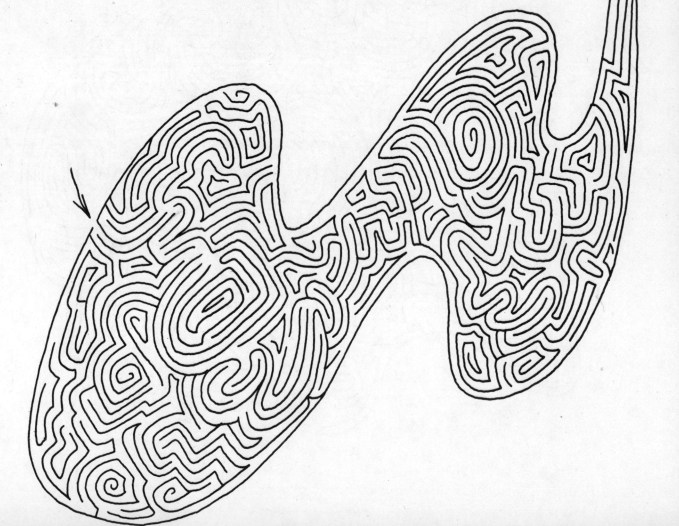

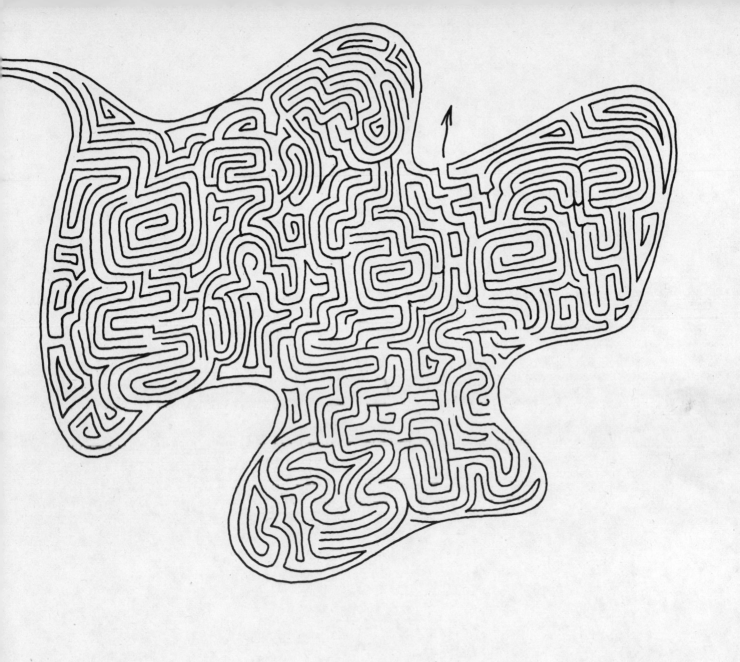

AGGRAVATION

Rated Time Limit: | **45 Minutes**

Maze 30

PUEBLO

Rated Time Limit: | 45 Minutes

ESCARGOT

Rated Time Limit: | **45 Minutes**

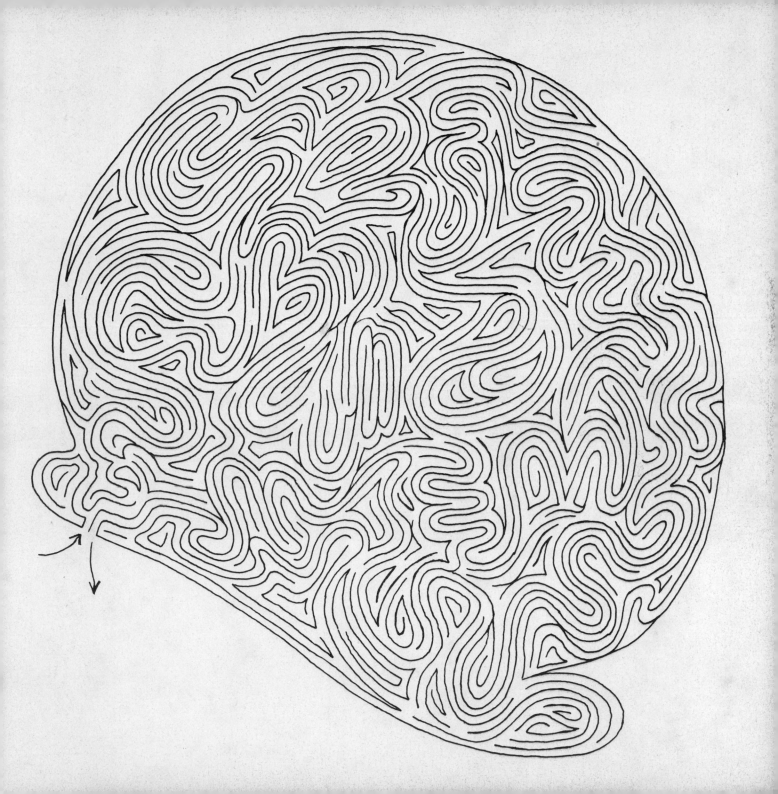

CURTAINS

| Rated Time Limit: | 45 Minutes |

GABRIEL

Rated Time Limit: | **45 Minutes**

Maze 34

CUL DE SAC?

Rated Time Limit: | **50 Minutes**

Maze 35

BULL RING

Rated Time Limit: | **55 Minutes**

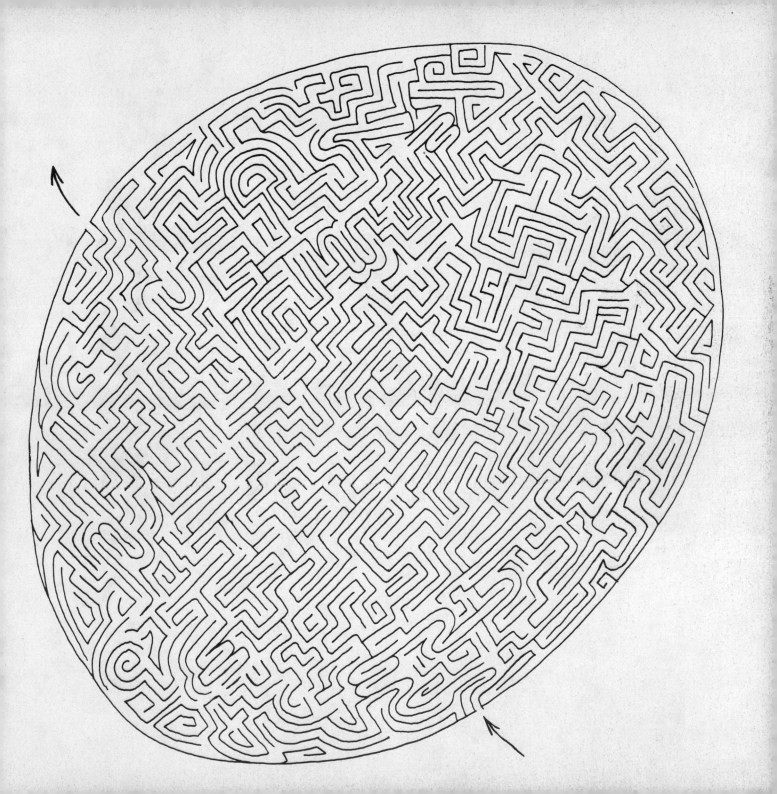

ZEPHYR

Rated Time Limit: | **55 Minutes**

Maze 37

DEVIOUS

Rated Time Limit: | *55 Minutes*

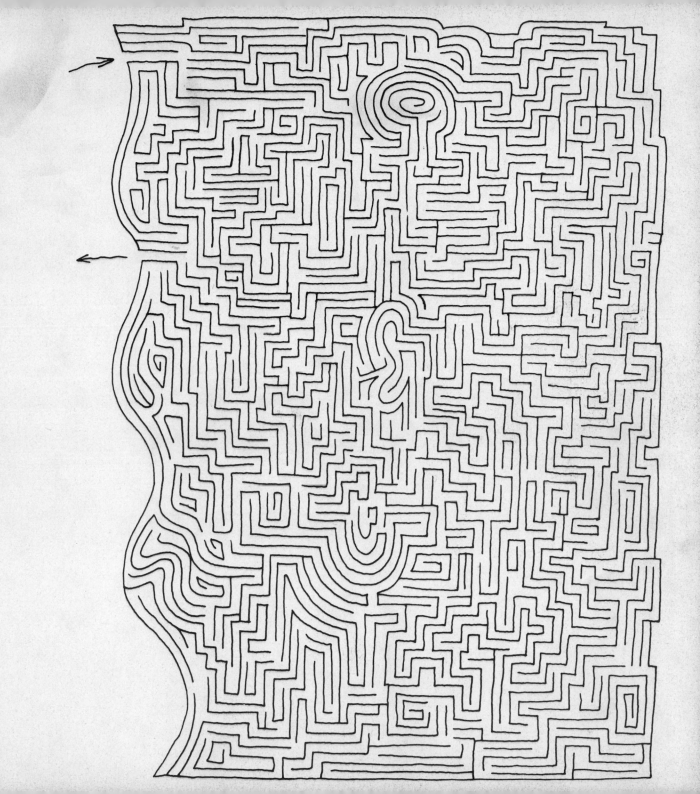

Maze 38

QUASAR

Rated Time Limit: | 60 Minutes

Maze 39
PERPLEXITY
Rated Time Limit: | **60 Minutes**

Maze 40

SISYPHUS

| Rated Time Limit: | 60 Minutes |

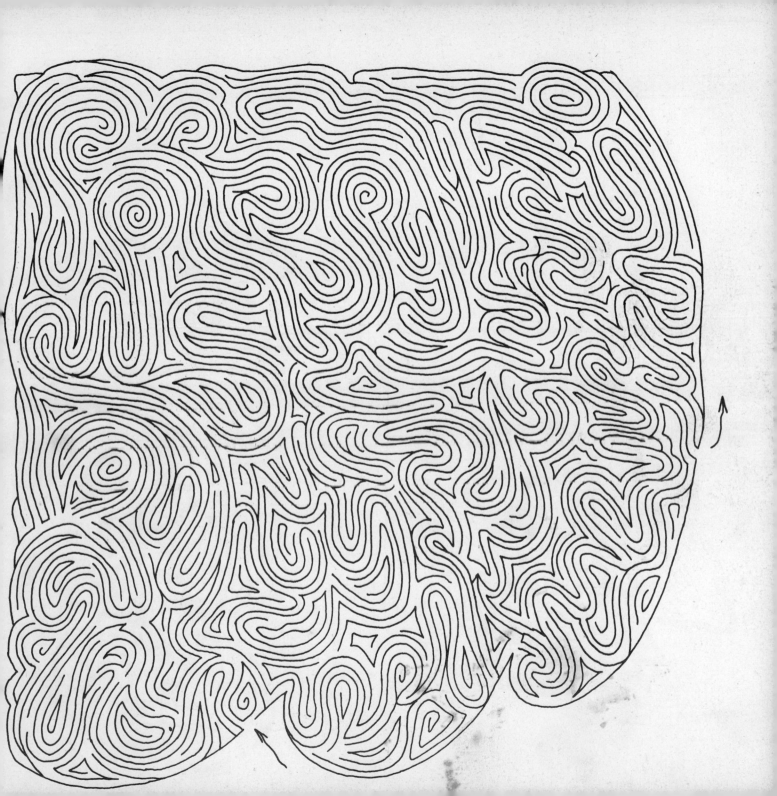

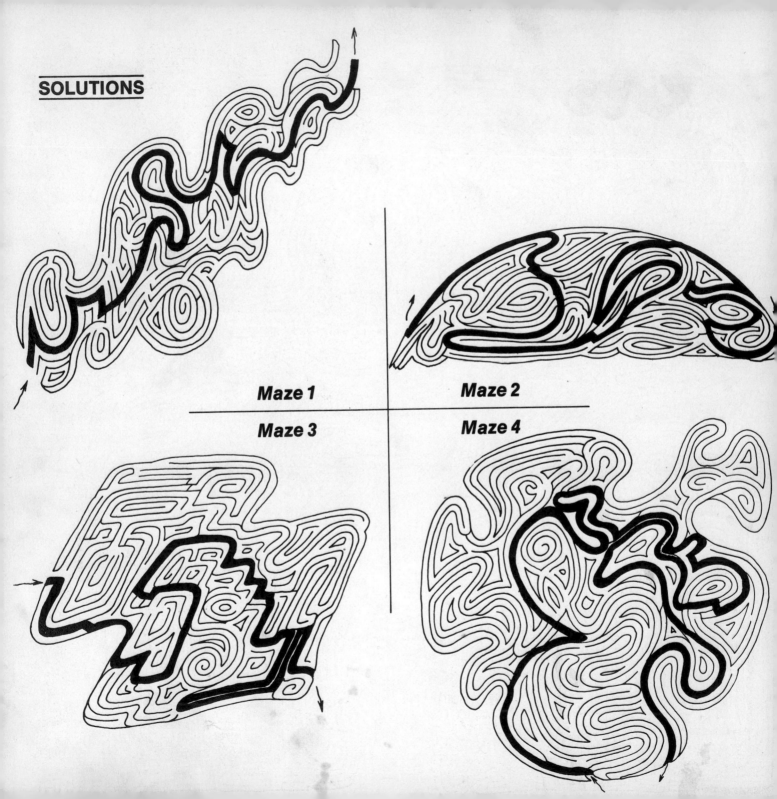

SOLUTIONS

Maze 1

Maze 2

Maze 3

Maze 4

Maze 5

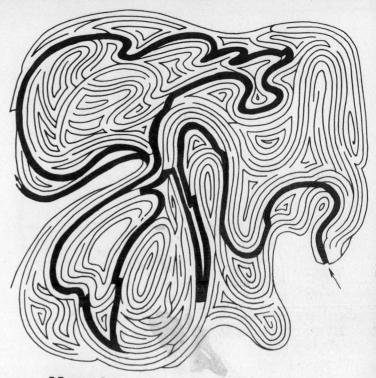

Maze 6

Maze 7

Maze 8

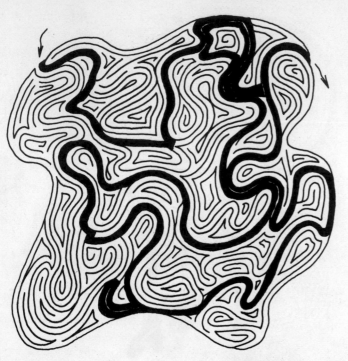

Maze 9

Maze 10

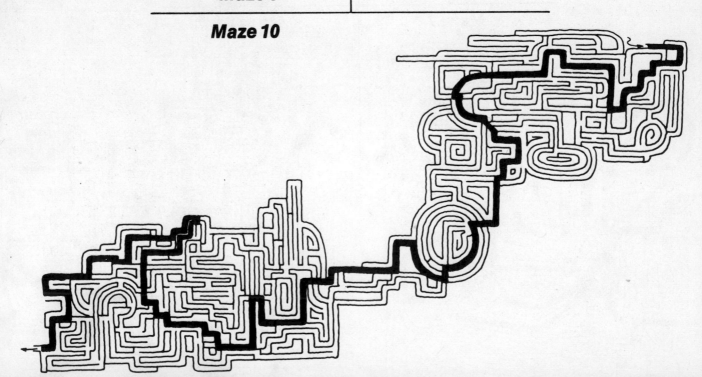

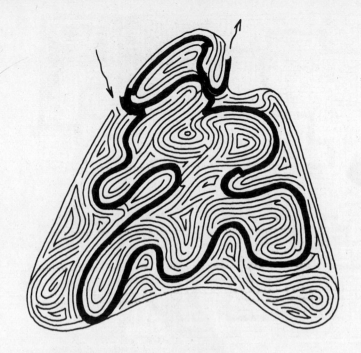

Maze 11

Maze 12

Maze 13

Maze 14

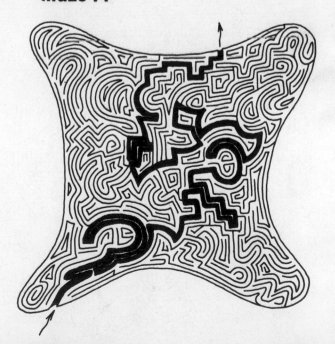

Maze 15

Maze 16

Maze 17

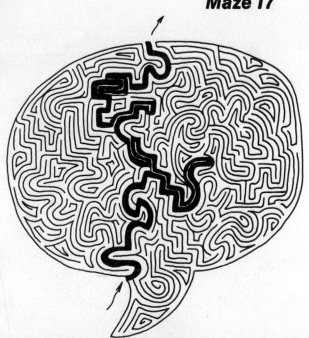

Maze 18

Maze 19

Maze 20

Maze 21

Maze 22

Maze 23

Maze 24

Maze 25

Maze 26

Maze 27

Maze 28

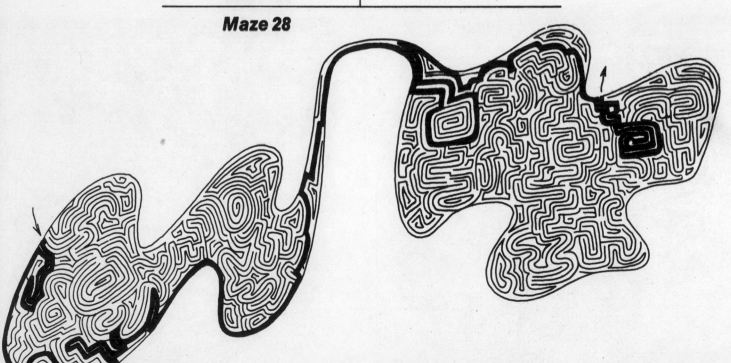

Maze 29

Maze 30

Maze 31

Maze 32

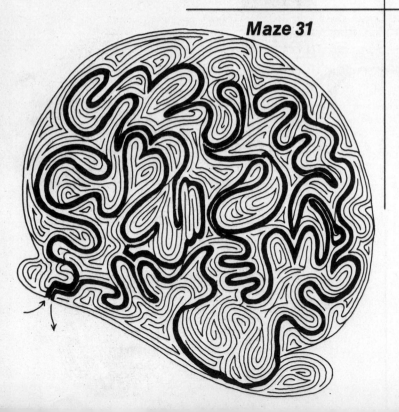

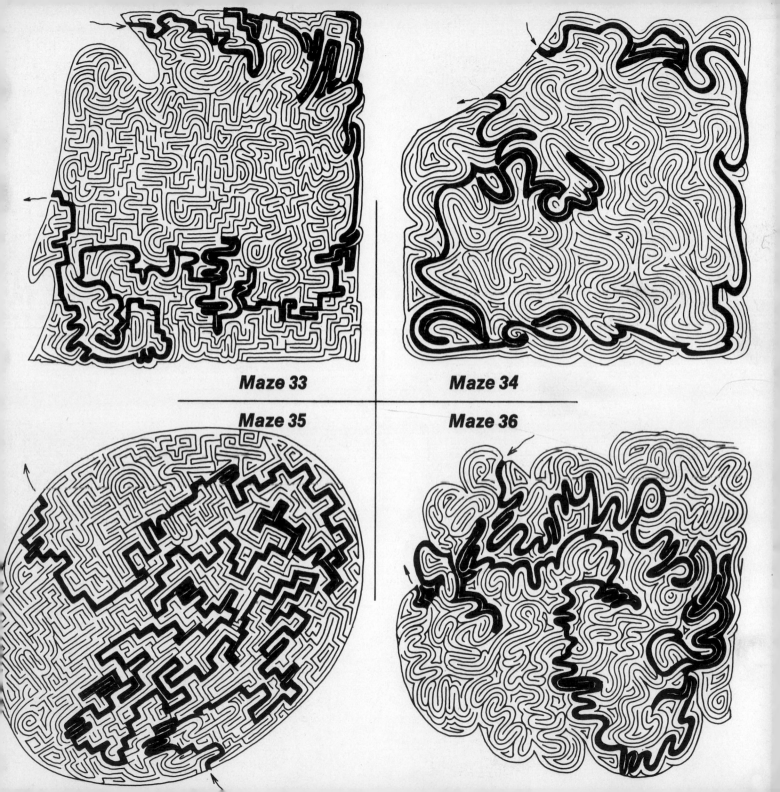

Maze 33

Maze 34

Maze 35

Maze 36

Maze 37

Maze 38

Maze 39

Maze 40

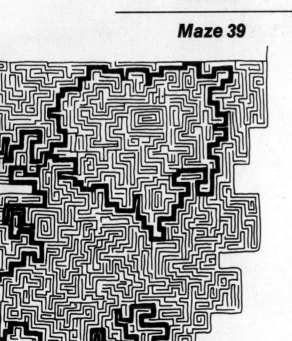

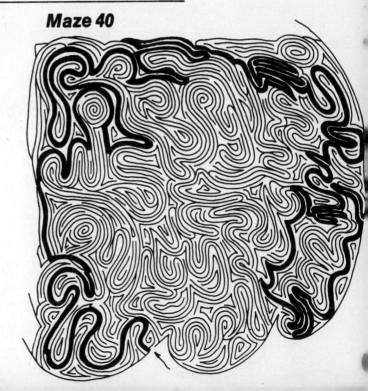